The Muddy Paws series

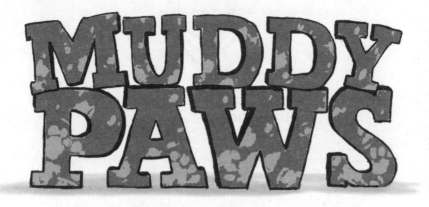

MUDDY PAWS

Saving Snowdrop

JENNY OLDFIELD

Illustrated by Paul Howard

Hodder
Children's
Books

A division of Hachette Children's Books

A Catalogue record for this book is available
from the British Library

ISBN 978 1 444 91321 7

Hodder Children's Books
A division of Hachette Children's Books
Hachette UK Limited
338 Euston Road,
London NW1 3BH
www.hachette.co.uk

To Lola, Jude and Evan – my little stars! JO

Chapter One

Whee! Smudge the brown and white school hamster sprinted happily inside his wheel. His little feet pitter-pattered, the wheel spun, Lexi and Lily smiled.

"He's fast," Lexi said.

"Very," Lily agreed.

"He could probably win a race in the Hamster Olympics."

"Definitely. He'd get the gold medal."

The girls couldn't take their eyes off Smudge's cage as he sprinted on.

"OK, Year 6." Mrs Taylor needed

everyone to pay attention. "Lily, Lexi – if you can tear yourselves away from Smudge and sit down in your seats, I have an important announcement to make."

Sighing, Lily and Lexi did as they were told.

Their teacher stood at the front of the class. She clapped her hands for everyone to quieten down. "Now, does anybody remember what's happening later this week?"

Sam Webster shot up his hand. "Miss, it's going to snow. It said so on the telly."

"Well, Sam – I wasn't thinking of that," Mrs Taylor said. "What else?"

"Miss, on Wednesday – Man United play Real Madrid!" Emma Watson cried. "It's the quarter-final of the UEFA Cup."

"No, not that either. Although the thing I'm talking about does happen on Wednesday

– the day after tomorrow." Mrs Taylor walked down the room until she came to the table which Tom Starling shared with Lily, Lexi and Charlie Jones. "Tom, I'm sure you know the answer to this. Why not remind the rest of the class?"

Shy Tom's face went red. "Please, Miss – you're all coming up to Moor Top Farm."

"Yeah!" Lexi grinned at Lily.

Tom lived at the farm with his mum and dad. It was open to visitors all year round.

Lily grinned back at Lexi. "The petting farm! How could we forget?"

"Because we're so busy at Muddy Paws – that's how," Lexi replied.

Left to themselves, the two cousins would look after people's pets from the moment they got up in the morning to the moment they went to bed at night. Lexi and Lily loved to work with animals – anything from naughty puppies who wouldn't do as they were told through piglets who ran away to homesick cats who refused to eat. That's what Muddy Paws did – it solved pet problems, big and small.

"Anyway – cool!" Lily sighed as she pictured the school trip to Moor Top Farm. There would be hens and chickens (her favourites), maybe cows and goats and definitely sheep.

"You'll need to bring a packed lunch to school on Wednesday," Mrs Taylor told the class as she got ready to begin the first lesson of the day. "And wrap up nice and warm – scarves, hats, gloves. Even though it's nearly spring, it's still going to be cold."

* * *

'Tom!' It was morning playtime and Lexi and Lily cornered him by the climbing-frame. "Tell us about your farm. What will we see?"

Tom tried to slide out of the corner. "The usual stuff," he grunted.

"What's wrong, Tom? Don't you want to talk to us?" a puzzled Lily asked.

"I'm meant to be playing footie with Emma," he explained.

"Emma's OK – she's playing with Sam and Charlie," Lexi said. "Come on, Tom – tell us about Moor Top Farm."

Tom gave in to pressure from the girls. "It's a petting farm," he muttered, his face turning red as they quizzed him.

"We already know that. What else?" Lily wanted to know. "Do you have chickens?"

"Yep."

"Cows?"

"Yep."

"Goats?"

"Nope."

"OK, then – sheep?" Lexi asked.

"'Course – yeah."

"How many?" "What type of sheep?" "What do they eat?" The questions came thick and fast because Lily and Lexi wanted to learn everything about the Starlings' farm. After all, everyone who knew them realized they were animal-mad.

Poor Tom blushed and tried to escape. When Emma dribbled by with the ball then cut back and passed it to him, he saw his chance to break free. He burst out of the corner, took the ball and passed it on to Sam Webster.

"Have you got any lambs?" Lexi called after him.

"Yep – three so far," he shouted over his shoulder.

"Wow!" Lily's smile went from ear to ear. "Three little lambs – already!"

"How cool is that!" Lexi agreed. "We're going to the petting farm and we're going to see three tiny, fluffy, white lambs!"

* * *

At home that night, Lexi sat at her dad's office table and updated the Muddy Paws website. Her little dog, Alfie, lay half asleep under her chair.

"Good news!" she typed. "We're going to visit a petting farm! If you don't know what that is – it's a farm where visitors can feed and stroke the animals and you can see lots of little chicks inside and then go outside and see pigs and donkeys and other sorts of farm animals."

Lexi's dad, James, ran a hand through her mass of dark brown curls. "I have to work away from home on Wednesday," he told her. "It sounds like fun though."

Lexi broke off from typing. "Will Alfie and me be staying with Lily?"

"Yes. I've already checked with Jo and Matt – they say it's fine with them."

"Good, 'cos Muddy Paws is really busy," she told him. "We can get through loads more appointments when I'm staying at Sea View."

James smiled. "So you won't miss me?"

Lexi grinned up at him. "No, we won't – will we, Alfie?"

Alfie cocked one silky, black ear. *Yip!* he said.

* * *

Meanwhile, over at Sea View Cottage, Lily was choosing her clothes for the Wednesday trip to the farm.

"Warm socks, woolly hat, gloves," she said out loud as she went into the kitchen to join her mum and dad. "Dad, have you seen my stripy socks?"

He looked up from his computer. "Are they stuffed inside your wellies?"

Lily went to look along the row of boots lined up by the back door. "Yup, here they are. And Mum, on Wednesday can I borrow your red scarf?"

"Sure," Jo replied. She sat in a warm corner watching the TV news. "It's hanging on the hook in the porch. And by the way, make sure you do wrap up really well," she added. "The weather lady is saying it's going to snow."

"I will," Lily promised. Come rain or shine, snow, ice, fog – whatever the weather threw at them – she could hardly wait for Wednesday and the school visit to Moor Top Farm.

Chapter Two

"I've been busy," Lexi announced when she called in at Sea View on her way to school next day. "I've got two more appointments for Muddy Paws." She took a red diary out of her bag. "Saturday morning at ten – we have to go into school and clean out Smudge's cage."

Lily nodded as she put on her padded jacket. "What else?"

"Teatime today – Miss Goodwin is bringing Dino for a pamper-session."

"That'll be fun." Lily picked up her

schoolbag and yelled goodbye to her dad, who was loading parcels of tea into the boot of the car. After a year of working from home, his speciality tea business was really taking off. Her mum was already busy in the café, baking scones and putting daffodils on the tables.

"So how many lambs will be born this year at Moor Top Farm?" Lexi wondered as she and Lily set off for school.

* * *

The first thing the girls did when they arrived was to say hi to Smudge.

Squeak-squeak-squeak. Smudge was busy with his morning exercise and didn't stop trundling inside his wheel to say hello.

When Mrs Taylor came into the room, they sat down at their table.

"Only one day to go until the school trip!"

Lexi whispered to Tom Starling. In her head she happily pictured fluffy yellow chicks, piglets with curly tails and of course the three newborn lambs.

He frowned and looked glum. "Yeah, and guess what?"

"What?" Lily asked. Why wasn't Tom happy about the class visit to his farm?

"Today Mrs Taylor is going to make me stand up and give a talk," he muttered as the teacher called out names from the register.

"A talk about your farm?" Lexi hissed at Tom.

He shuffled in his seat. "Yeah – she wants me to tell people about the lambs."

"For our Moor Top Farm project?" Lily asked.

He nodded. "I have to say how they're born and all that stuff."

Lily and Lexi could see this wouldn't be easy for Tom. The farmer's son was the quiet, thoughtful type who liked to sit at the back of the class. He wasn't exactly unfriendly – just shy.

As the time for his talk drew near, they watched him take a sheet of paper out of his bag and hold it between trembling hands.

"Stand up, Tom," Mrs Taylor instructed kindly. "Speak in a nice, clear voice."

His face turned deep red as he started to read. "'How Lambs Are Born'," he began. "'Most lambs are born between February and April. We bring the pregnant ewes into a field near the farmyard.'"

Lily took notes. She wanted to remember every single thing he told them.

"'One hour before the ewe gives birth, she leaves the flock and looks for a quiet corner. The lamb is born head first. Once the head and shoulders come out, the rest is very quick. The head is covered in a slimy coating called the mucus membrane.'"

"Yuck!" Emma muttered under her breath.

"Sshh!" Lexi warned.

"'The mother licks the lamb's face clean. After twenty minutes the lamb begins to suck.'" As Tom came to the end of his talk, he slowed down and looked up from his paper. "Is that OK, Miss? I took pictures of our first three lambs. Do you want to see them?"

"Yes please, Tom," Mrs Taylor said. "Give them to me at playtime and I'll stick them on the notice-board." She smiled at him. "Well done and thank you very much. Now we can all look forward to meeting the lambs at Moor Top Farm, remembering everything you've told us."

* * *

The whole school went out to play, then as soon as playtime was finished, Lily and Lexi rushed back into the classroom and looked eagerly at Tom's photos. Each picture showed a pure white woolly lamb.

"What are they called?" they wanted to know.

Tom shrugged. "We get so many lambs we don't give them names."

"But *we* can," Lexi decided. "We could have a class vote. Let's ask Mrs Taylor."

"Good idea," the teacher said when Lily and Lexi suggested it to her. "Everyone think of a name, write it down, fold up your piece of paper and pop it into my felt-tip pen box. We'll pick out three and they'll be the names we'll give to Tom's lambs."

"Mary." Lily wrote carefully on her scrap of paper. Just like the girl in the nursery rhyme. " 'Mary had a little lamb . . .' "

Lexi thought hard then wrote down her suggestion. "Snowdrop." She crossed her fingers as she dropped her paper into the box.

After the whole class had finished, Mrs Taylor asked Tom to pick out the first piece of paper.

"Will you read it, Miss?" he asked shyly.

" 'Amy'," the teacher announced, pinning the name next to the first picture. "Next?"

"Mary," Lily muttered, hoping that her name would come out of the box.

" '. . . Skippy'," Mrs Taylor announced, pinning up the second choice.

Lily felt a little disappointed.

"Snowdrop." Lexi kept her fingers crossed and silently mouthed her chosen name.

"'. . . Snowdrop'," Mrs Taylor said.

"Yes!" Lexi grinned. Her suggestion had been picked out of the box. How lucky was that!

"That's a good name," Lily admitted as they went back to their seats. Really – Snowdrop was a great name for a lamb, and so were Amy and Skippy. Yes, everything was cool and the best thing was – tomorrow was almost here!

* * *

"Hello, girls." That afternoon Daisy Goodwin breezed into the garden at Sea View Cottage, carrying her white Persian cat in a pet carrier. "We're ready for our pamper-session, aren't we, Dino?"

Lexi and Lily had already put on their
Muddy Paws T-shirts and were throwing
sticks for Alfie. Alfie bounded across the
smooth lawn, growled at the stick, seized it
between his teeth then tossed it in the air
and caught it again. "Hi, Miss Goodwin!"
Lily called. "Bring Dino into the kitchen."

"I'll put Alfie in the living room." Lexi
knew that Dino wasn't used to dogs so it was
best to keep him and Alfie in separate rooms.

Soon Lily had spread a towel on the kitchen table and Lexi settled Miss Goodwin's long-haired cat on top of it. "Comb or brush?" she asked Lily.

"You comb, I'll brush," Lily decided.

"I'm afraid Dino's coat is a little tangled," his owner sighed as she watched Lexi gently tease the comb through his long hair.

"Oops – a big knot!" Lexi declared as she teased it out of the cat's coat. "Stay still, Dino. There – that's a good boy."

Lily stood by with a brush. While she waited she began to tell their grey-haired visitor all about next day's school trip. "Honestly, it'll be great," she promised. "There'll be piglets and chickens for a start."

"Hmm." Miss Goodwin sounded interested. "I've heard that the Starlings have worked hard to improve visitor numbers to the petting farm."

"There we go, Dino," Lexi said as she handed him over to Lily. Lily began to brush and smiled when Dino half closed his green eyes and started to purr.

"I must pay a visit to Moor Top Farm," Miss Goodwin decided. "But I think I'll wait until the weather gets warmer."

Lily brushed Dino while Lexi and Miss Goodwin chatted on. Dino purred. The stove in the corner made the Sea View kitchen warm and cosy. Outside, a few flakes of snow began to fall.

Chapter Three

When Lexi woke next morning, it took a while to remember where she was.

Alfie was asleep at the foot of the bed, the flowery curtains in Sea View Cottage's guest bedroom were drawn, and it was still dark outside.

There was a knock at the bedroom door then Lily came in already dressed. "Time to get up," she told Lexi as she pulled the duvet off the bed.

"Urgh! What day is it?" Lexi mumbled.

"Wednesday – Moor Top Farm, remember!"

Lexi was out of bed in a flash. She rushed to put on her clothes. "No, Alfie!" she protested when he tried to grab one of her boots. "No time to play!"

Lily grinned and ran downstairs. Her mum was in the kitchen making two packed lunches and her dad stirred porridge on the stove. "We're going to see pigs and chickens!" Lily sang out. "We'll meet Amy, Skippy and Snowdrop!"

Her dad stopped stirring. "Have you looked outside yet?" he asked.

"No – why?" She ran to the door and flung it open. "Oh!"

A gust of cold air blew into the kitchen. Still carrying Lexi's boot in his mouth, Alfie sprinted down the stairs, across the kitchen and out on to the lawn.

"Alfie, stop!" Lexi was close on his heels. But she stopped by Lily at the back door.

"Oh!" she echoed.

The green lawn was white and the pond was frozen over. Snow had fallen on the café roof and on the roof of the car, on the branches of the trees, along the wall tops and out in the lane.

"It snowed," Lily said in a worried voice.

"What's wrong, girls? I thought you liked the snow," Jo said.

"We do," Lexi sighed. Normally they loved to build snowmen, throw snowballs and go sledging . . .

"But . . ." Lily groaned. "Does this mean they'll cancel our trip?"

How would the school bus get up the steep lane to Moor Top Farm? Would it even be open on a day like today?

"I don't know," her mum replied. "But why don't we drive to school to find out?"

"The sky's nice and blue," Lexi pointed out as she and Lily sat in the back seat of Jo's car.

"The sun's shining," Lily added hopefully.

"And look – the snow is already melting," Jo said as the school came into view.

The bus was waiting in the playground and Mrs Taylor stood at the gates. "Good morning, Lily. Good morning, Lexi," she said as the girls got out of the car. "Have you remembered your packed lunches?"

They nodded eagerly. "Does that mean we're still going to Moor Top Farm?" Lexi asked.

"Of course," their teacher answered cheerfully as she ticked their names on the register. "The petting farm is open for business as usual. A little bit of snow isn't going to stop us."

"Phew!" Lily felt her worries melt away.

"Cool!" Lexi said, racing to be first on the bus.

* * *

Lily and Lexi sat happily on the back seat as the bus wound its way up the hill. Lily cleared a small patch on the steamed-up window. She caught a glimpse of the sea sparkling in the distance. "Brrr – look at those poor sheep!" she said with a shiver.

Lexi spotted the few sheep huddled under a tree. They were cold and miserable. "Let's hope Amy, Skippy and Snowdrop are snuggled up in a nice warm barn," she said.

Lily agreed. She was glad when the bus turned off the narrow lane into a car park and Mrs Taylor stood up to tell everyone they'd arrived.

"We'll head straight for the main barn,"

she instructed. "Everyone stay together until we're inside."

Lexi and Lily could hardly wait. They filed off the bus and saw a white farmhouse and a big stone barn.

"Where's Tom?" Lily wondered. She'd expected to see the farmer's son waiting for them in the car park.

"He's sick," Mrs Taylor told her. "He has a cough and a cold. His mum phoned the school secretary early this morning. I'm afraid he'll have to stay at home for the rest of the week."

In the field next to the house Lexi spotted some more sheep, and in a paddock beside the barn she saw two donkeys eating hay from a metal feeder. "Wow – donkeys!" she cried.

She hadn't expected this and was about to

run across the car park for a closer look when Mrs Taylor reminded her to stay with the group.

"You can see the donkeys later," she told Lexi. "Come inside with the others."

"Wow – sheep!" Lily wanted to head off in the other direction. "And two lambs!"

The babies were with their mother, who stood close to the gate.

"Later, Lily!" Mrs Taylor warned.

So Lily and Lexi followed the rest of their class into the barn, where Tom's dad, Fred Starling, greeted them.

"Welcome to Moor Top Farm," he said in a deep, slow voice. He was a tall man with wavy, fair hair, dressed in a blue jumper and jacket, with jeans and boots. "Now I know you're all dying to stroke the guinea pigs and see some chicks, so off you go and have fun."

Lexi and Lily grinned at each other. The barn looked exciting. Straight ahead there was a pen made from straw bales with a dozen guinea pigs inside. Then there were other pens with proper wooden fences where piglets lay next to their mothers in straw beds. Notices told you the names of the pigs.

"This one's called Honeysuckle." Lily had made a bee-line for a white pig with black patches, just like Roxy and Rosie, the Goldings' piglets from Lane's End. Last summer she and Lexi had looked after the two little piglets when Emma and Charlie Golding went away.

Oink! Honeysuckle rustled through the straw and poked her snout through the fence railings. She snuffled at Lily's pockets, greedy eyes gleaming.

"There's nothing in there!" Lily protested.

Anyway, there was a notice saying "Do Not Feed the Animals!"

"Lily, come and look!" Lexi cried. She was in a far corner of the barn, beside a big, brightly-lit glass box containing about fifty yellow chicks. She didn't wait for Lily to arrive before she moved on.

"Aah!" Lily stopped to stare at the three-day-old chicks. They were super-cute, with fluffy feathers and tiny beaks. They made a loud cheep-cheeping noise.

"Lily!" Lexi insisted.

Lily tore herself away from the chicks and joined Lexi beside a pen lit by a large heat lamp. The floor was strewn with lettuce leaves, carrots, leeks, broccoli – a whole greengrocer's shop full of vegetables. "Whoa!" she said when she saw what Lexi wanted to show her.

" 'Meet Darwin, the giant tortoise.' " Lexi read the notice on the wall. " 'Our new arrival weighs in at 200 kilograms. He's seventy years old and eats grass and leaves. He likes nothing better than to take a nap in the sun.' "

"Whoa!" Lily said again. For once she was speechless.

Darwin was enormous. His bumpy, humped shell was as big as a small bathtub and he lumbered slowly across his pen with his thin, leathery neck stretched out and his beady eyes fixed on the girls.

"He's older than my gran!" Lexi breathed.

"He's older than anything!" Lily said.

"Look, he's coming towards us!" Though Lexi was animal-mad, even she wasn't sure how close she wanted to get to the ginormous tortoise.

"Don't worry – he won't hurt you," Fred Starling said. The friendly farmer came up and tipped a fresh load of lettuce leaves into the pen.

"He's . . . amazing," Lily told him when she at last found the right word. Like nothing she'd ever seen before.

"Feeding Darwin is usually Tom's job," Fred said. "But today he's had to stay in bed. He's really upset about it."

"We knew he was sick – our teacher told us." Watching Darwin tuck into the fresh lettuce leaves made Lexi a bit less scared. After all, he was like any other tortoise, only fifty times as big.

Lily felt sorry for Tom but she decided to change the subject. "Mr Starling, there were only two lambs out in the field."

"Yes, that would be the first twins of the year. They were born last Sunday. We're still waiting for the next lot – it should be any day now."

Lily frowned. "So that must have been Amy and Skippy, but what about Snowdrop? Where's she?"

"Ah." Fred paused. "There's a small problem with Snowdrop. Didn't Tom say?"

Lexi and Lily shook their heads. They suddenly felt worried. Staring up at the farmer, they waited for him to go on.

"The fact is, her mother died giving birth to a second lamb. It all happened before dawn on Monday morning so there was no one around to lend a hand."

"Oh!" Lexi sighed. "Did the other lamb die too?"

Fred nodded. "So Snowdrop is an orphan," Fred said. "It's tough for lambs who lose their mothers. We don't even know if Snowdrop will survive – it's touch and go."

Chapter Four

For the next part of the morning, Lily and Lexi joined their group on a tour of the petting farm. They tried hard to forget what the farmer had told them about the little orphan lamb, but she kept popping back into their minds.

"I hope Snowdrop will be OK," Lexi whispered as the class watched a video about the farming year. It showed a field full of spring flowers with lambs happily running and jumping.

Lily stared at the big screen. Now the

video showed two lambs suckling while their mother grazed quietly. When the youngsters had finished feeding, they skipped off through the green grass to play.

"That's how it should be," she sighed, thinking of Snowdrop without a mum.

Then the video finished and Mrs Taylor put them into pairs and sent them off with observation sheets attached to a clipboard.

"Yuck, look at all these questions!" Lexi complained as she read the sheet.

"Yeah – and they're all about animals – every single one. It's great, isn't it?" If Lily kept busy, she managed to put Snowdrop out of her mind.

She crossed the barn and stopped by a pen surrounded by a chicken-wire fence. Inside she counted twenty-five rabbits of all shapes and sizes. She read a question from the sheet. "'How many Dwarf Lops can you find?'"

Lexi was already counting the pale fawn bunnies. "Seven," she reported.

"Seven" Lily wrote in the box. "'How many black and white Himalayans?'"

"Five, six, seven, eight, nine." Lexi counted carefully and once more Lily wrote down the answer. She liked the skinny Himalayan rabbits with their pink eyes better than the chubby Dwarf Lops but not as much as the Netherland Dwarfs with their cute round heads and short ears.

"OK, we've finished the rabbit section," Lexi said. "What's next?"

Lily looked at the sheet. "Donkeys," she said.

* * *

Donkeys then cows. Lily and Lexi scooted outside. Shivering and trying to ignore the cold, they ran from field to field. They splashed through muddy puddles along tracks where snow had recently melted, answering all the questions on their observation sheet.

"'What are the names of the two Moor Top Farm donkeys?'" Lily asked through chattering teeth. Brrr!

Lexi read the notice on the paddock gate and gave her the answer. "Venus and Serena." Brrr!

As Lily wrote down the names, Venus stopped eating hay from the feeder, threw back her head, bared her teeth and brayed. *Eee-aawww!*

The girls covered their ears then laughed and moved on to the field with the cows. "'Which breed of cattle has long, shaggy hair and big, curved horns?' "

Brrr! "Highland cattle."

They were doing well – more than halfway through the set of questions.

"Time to sneak another quick peek at Darwin?" Lexi suggested.

The girls dashed back inside and were chatting with the giant tortoise when Fred Starling came up to them. He carried a bottle full of what looked like milk.

"Hello again," he began. "You were the girls who asked me about the orphan lamb – right?"

They nodded.

"I was wondering – would you like to watch me feed her?"

His question took Lily by surprise. "Would we . . . ?"

"Definitely!" Lexi jumped in.

"Follow me," Fred said with a grin. And he led them out of the barn, across a yard and into a quiet, cold outhouse. "We don't usually allow the public to come in here," he explained, "but you two seemed interested in Snowdrop and I thought you'd like to meet her."

"Where is she?" Lexi asked. The light was dim and at first she could see anything except a small pen with straw on the floor.

"There!" Lily said softly. The lamb lay with her front legs folded under her, looking up at her visitors from her straw bed.

"Hey, little girl," Fred said as he went into the pen. He slid his broad hand under Snowdrop's tummy and lifted her up. "Time for a drink."

"She looks light as a feather," Lexi murmured.

43

"Monday, Tuesday, Wednesday – just three days old." Lily's eyes were glued to Snowdrop as Fred made sure the rubber teat was firmly attached to the bottle of milk before he slid it into the lamb's mouth.

"This bottle has to be sterilized," he told the girls. "The milk is a special formula, not just ordinary cows' milk."

"Doesn't she like it?" Lexi asked. Milk was dribbling from the corners of Snowdrop's mouth and it didn't seem as if the baby sheep wanted to suck.

"It takes them a while to get used to the teat. Tom usually does this for me, so he's better at it than I am."

They watched anxiously for a while.

"That's better," Lily murmured as Snowdrop began to drink. Over the next few minutes she watched the lamb slowly empty the bottle.

"Good girl," Fred said. He gently slid the teat out of her mouth then invited Lexi and Lily into the pen. "Would you like to stroke her?" he offered.

Lily ran her hand along Snowdrop's woolly back. "Soft!" she breathed.

Snowdrop gazed back at her and gave a small, high bleat.

Then it was Lexi's turn. She rubbed the top of the lamb's bony head.

Ba-a-a-a! Snowdrop bleated.

"Time for her to sleep," Fred said quietly as he laid her back in the straw.

* * *

That evening, Lily and Lexi had lots to add to their Muddy Paws website.

They posted pictures of Highland cattle standing in a snowy field and of Venus the donkey throwing back her head and braying. They explained the difference between Dwarf Lop rabbits (who weren't really dwarfs) and Netherland Dwarfs (who were).

"A totally brilliant thing happened today." Lexi typed while Lily picked Alfie up to show him the computer screen. "Mr Starling let us stroke Snowdrop ☺ ☺"

Lily grinned. "You hear that, Alfie? Tom's dad let us feed an orphan lamb!"

Yip! Lexi's little dog licked Lily's hand with his rough pink tongue.

"He did!" Lily insisted. "Snowdrop is so cu-u-ute!"

Lexi typed on. "We watched him feed her from a bottle. No one else was there – just me and Lily from Muddy Paws!"

Chapter Five

"What time did you two get to sleep last night?" Matt asked Lily and Lexi next morning as he walked to school with them. "It must have been late because we heard you chatting in Lily's room after we went to bed."

Lexi yawned and left it to Lily to explain. "Lexi came to tell me that we've got a new client for Muddy Paws. She forgot to do it earlier."

"Her name's Kylie," Lexi added. "I talked to her owner on the phone. He wants us to dog-sit for a few hours."

"Kylie, eh?" Matt was used to strange dogs running around the garden at Sea View Cottage. He waved the girls off across the frosty playground. "What type of dog is she?" he asked. "When is she coming to Muddy Paws?"

But the girls were too far away to hear.

"I suppose I'll find out soon enough," he said to himself as he walked on to the post office.

* * *

After the visit to Moor Top Farm, Mrs Taylor kept her class busy all through Thursday and Friday with follow-up work. They made charts and drew pictures, wrote a diary of the day, chose their favourite animals and looked up information on the internet.

Lily wrote:

My favourite animal was Snowdrop. With orphan lambs you have to feed them every four hours for the first four or five days, then after that it's every six to eight hours. You feed them one pint at first, going up to three pints by the time they're weaned at six weeks.

"Very good, Lily," Mrs Taylor said when she saw what Lily was writing. "And Lexi – I see you've chosen Snowdrop as your favourite animal too."

Lexi handed her paper to the teacher.

"'Lambs are dead cute. When a lamb loses its mother, it's called an orphan lamb,'" she read out. "'The farmer has to hand-rear them. You have to put them in a clean, straw-lined pen and make sure they stay warm.'"

"The problem was – Snowdrop didn't like to drink from the bottle," Lexi explained to Mrs Taylor. "Mr Starling said that Tom was better at feeding her than he was but he was too poorly."

Mrs Taylor glanced at the empty seat across the table from Lily and Lexi. "Yes, it's bad luck that he's fallen ill right now."

"How come?" Lexi asked as she began to draw a lamb in a green field filled with red and yellow flowers.

"Lambing season is the busiest time of year for the Starlings. Tom's dad needs all the help he can get."

* * *

"Hello, Arthur!" It was Friday afternoon and Matt was surprised to find Arthur Bolton, the owner of Shilton Books, standing at the door of Sea View Cottage.

In the kitchen Lily and Lexi were busy doing their homework, putting finishing touches to their Moor Top Farm folders.

"What brings you here?" Matt asked the owner of the online book-selling business.

Hearing voices, Lexi dashed to the door. "It's OK, Uncle Matt – Mr Bolton has brought Kylie to Muddy Paws. Oh . . ." She looked around and saw that the visitor was alone. "Where's Kylie?" she asked.

"Erm, I left her in the car." Mr Bolton seemed uneasy. "Are you sure you want to dog-sit while I go to an early evening concert in town?" he asked Matt.

"It's nothing to do with me," Matt explained with a smile. "Lily and Lexi run Muddy Paws all by themselves."

"It's cold in the car so let's bring her in!" Lexi said eagerly. She called for Lily and

Alfie to join them then they all walked up the path and across the car park to meet their latest client.

"Kylie is a little – erm – nervous around other dogs." Mr Bolton came to a halt beside his shabby yellow car. He frowned as he glanced down at Alfie.

"Oh, Alfie's fine," Lily said quickly. "He's very friendly."

Alfie heard his name and wagged his tail. He sat down quietly beside Lexi.

"It's just that Kylie . . . well, she can be a little hard to handle."

"It's OK, honestly." Lexi was impatient to meet Arthur Bolton's dog. "We'll look after her, no problem. What time will you be back to collect her?"

"I'll only be gone for three hours," Arthur promised. He was small and thin, with a dark, pointed beard and long hair that curled over his jacket collar. "But I don't like to leave her alone in the house – she gets miserable without me."

"It's OK," Lily insisted. "Muddy Paws is happy to help."

"If you say so." Reluctantly Mr Bolton opened the driver's door to let Kylie out.

Whoosh! A black and brown ball of silky fur leaped out. *Yip-yap-yip!* Floppy ears flying, the little King Charles spaniel exploded on to the Sea View lawn.

"Kylie, come here!" Arthur Bolton called while Alfie looked on with a puzzled expression.

Kylie yipped and yapped her way around the frozen fish-pond.

"Stop! Come here!" her owner yelled. "Oh no!" he cried when Kylie suddenly

changed course, leaped on to the ice and
skidded right across the pond.

"Oops!" Lily said.

Kylie couldn't stop skidding. She skated
and scrabbled, slid and spun.

"It's OK, I'll get her," Lexi promised.
"Stay, Alfie," she said as she dashed to the
rescue.

Alfie stayed. He looked interested to see

how this would turn out.

Lexi reached the pond in time to hear a loud crack. Oh no – the ice was breaking!

Sure enough, Kylie had made a hole in the ice. Her back legs disappeared into the water and Lexi was just in time to grab her and scoop her out.

"We'll need a towel to dry her off," Lily told Alfie.

Lexi's dog looked wise and cocked his head to one side.

"No problem – I'll do it," Lexi called. And she quickly disappeared with Kylie into the cottage.

"I'm really not sure about this," Arthur sighed.

"Kylie will be fine with us," Lily promised.

"If I didn't already have a ticket for the concert . . ."

"Go!" Lily told him. She didn't give him chance to change his mind before she set off with Alfie across the lawn.

* * *

Inside the house, Lexi rubbed Kylie dry with a soft, striped towel.

Grrrr! Kylie complained. When Lexi lifted the towel and let her jump down from the chair, she darted straight at Alfie, teeth bared. *Grrrrr!* she said.

"Ignore her," Lily told Alfie. "She's only trying to tell you that she's top dog."

"She's sweet though," Matt said.

In fact, Kylie was gorgeous. She had a long, wavy, brown and black coat and lovely floppy ears, plus the biggest, brownest eyes you could imagine.

Grrr! Kylie told Matt.

* * *

Yip-yap! Kylie barked at Jo when she came in from the café at the end of the afternoon. She ran and jumped up – once, twice, three times.

"Down!" Jo said.

Kylie jumped and yapped.

"Super-sweet," Matt said with a smile as he stirred the pasta sauce for supper.

"No, Dad – it's not sweet!" Lily was cross with him. "If a big dog like a Doberman jumped up like that, no way would you say it was sweet."

"True," Jo agreed. "It's only because she's tiny." She backed off from Kylie, who decided to chase Alfie around the kitchen table instead.

"It's called Small Dog Syndrome," Lily said seriously. "That's when a small dog like a King Charles spaniel or a Chihuahua believes he's a big dog."

"The leader of the pack." Lexi helped Lily to explain. "They develop bad habits and the owner doesn't stop them because they think it's cute."

"That's too deep for me," Matt said with a smile. "You two are the pet psychologists. Now, who's for spaghetti bolognese?"

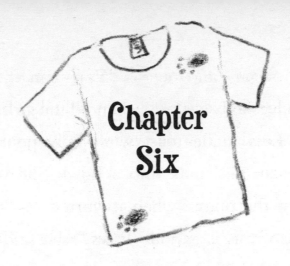

Chapter Six

"Kylie certainly was a handful." Jo was awake early next morning and was already in the kitchen when Lexi and Lily came downstairs. "A small dog who thinks she's the boss, eh, Alfie?"

Alfie wagged his tail.

"Anyway, Arthur was pleased with Muddy Paws," Lily told her mum. "He said he'd use us again next time he needs a dog-sitter."

"Very good," Jo said absent-mindedly. She was thinking about the day ahead, about baking cakes for the café and ordering more flour, sugar and eggs. "You can help yourselves to breakfast," she told the girls.

So Lexi made toast while Lily poured cornflakes and milk into a bowl. She was nearest the phone when it started to ring. "Hello – this is Muddy Paws," she said in her best Muddy Paws voice.

"This is Tom Starling. Who's that?" the croaky voice on the other end of the line asked.

"Oh hi, Tom. Lily here."

"OK, good. Listen . . ."

"You don't sound very well," Lily interrupted. "Is your throat still sore? Shouldn't you be in bed?"

"I am in bed," he admitted. "But listen – I want to know what you're doing this morning."

"Going into school to feed Smudge and clean out his cage. Then we have to wash our Muddy Paws T-shirts then take Alfie for a walk . . ." Lily began the list.

"Right." Tom sounded disappointed. "So you don't have time to come up here?"

"I never said that. Anyway, what for?" Lily switched on the speakerphone and invited Lexi to listen in.

"It's Snowdrop," Tom croaked. "Dad says she still isn't feeding properly."

"And you want us to help?" Lexi said quickly with a mouth full of toast and marmalade.

"If you've got time."

"Definitely!" Lily told him.

"We'll be right there," Lexi promised.

* * *

"It's lucky Dad was free to give us a lift," Lily said to Lexi as they waved Matt off from the car park at Moor Top Farm. "It would have taken ages to make it up the hill on our bikes."

It was a crisp, sunny Saturday morning and the place was busy with visitors queuing to see Honeysuckle, the chicks, guinea pigs, rabbits and of course the new star attraction – Darwin.

"Oh gosh, look – lots of new lambs have been born since we were here on Wednesday!" Lexi pointed to the long-legged babies skipping and jumping in the sloping field next to the house. "One, two, three, four, five, six!" she counted.

The sight of the lambs playing in the fresh air alongside their mums only made Lily even more anxious about orphan Snowdrop. She spotted Fred Starling at the entrance to the barn and ran up to him.

He greeted them with a warm smile.

"Hello, girls. Tom said you might drop by."

"How's Snowdrop?" Lexi asked him hurriedly. Her warm breath made clouds of steam in the cold air.

"Come and see for yourselves." Quickly he led the way across the barn.

"Hi, Honeysuckle," Lily said to the Gloucester Old Spot as they ran to keep up.

Oink! Honeysuckle pushed her snout through the fence rails. Oink!

"Hi, Darwin," Lexi said to the giant tortoise who oh-so-slowly raised his flat, scaly head and watched in silence as they dashed past.

Fred took them through the back door, across the cobbled yard and into the outhouse. "It's time for another feed," he told the girls as he took a bottle from his jacket pocket. "I'm pushed for time this morning. Would you two like to try?"

"That's why we're here," Lily said eagerly. "We told Tom we'd help."

"We'll do anything you ask us to do," Lexi assured him. "Just so long as Snowdrop doesn't mind."

* * *

"We have to be really quiet," Lily murmured to Lexi as she carried the bottle of milk into Snowdrop's pen.

"And not do anything sudden," Lexi agreed.

The lamb raised her head and let out a high-pitched bleat.

"It's OK," Lexi whispered. She decided to sit down in the straw and watch Lily feed the lamb. She sat so still that in the far corner of the outhouse a small grey mouse crept out from under a stack of upturned flowerpots

and scurried across the stone floor.

"Here's some yummy milk." Lily crouched beside Snowdrop to show her the bottle. "I'm just going to pick you up – ever so gently – and while I cuddle you to keep you warm, you're going to glug-glug-glug the whole of this bottle!"

Ba-a-a-a! Snowdrop bleated again. But

she didn't resist when Lily picked her up and pressed the teat against the lamb's lips.

"Careful – the milk's dribbling out," Lexi warned.

"Come on – open your mouth," Lexi whispered. She was worried because Snowdrop's little body felt terribly thin and she weighed hardly anything.

"Don't force her," Lexi urged. "Look – she's licking her lips. You can slide the teat inside her mouth now – cool, you did it!"

"At last!" Lily felt the baby lamb tug at the teat and begin to suck.

"She's really hungry," Lexi murmured. The sight of Snowdrop drinking the milk from the bottle was sad and wonderful at the same time. Somehow it made Lexi want to cry.

"Phone Tom and tell him how we're

getting on," Lily suggested.

Lexi took out her phone and found Tom's number. "Hi, Tom. We're with Snowdrop. Lily did it – she got her to take the milk."

"Cool," Tom croaked. "But wait a minute – you mean Dad let you two give her the bottle – right?"

"Yeah – that's OK with you, isn't it?" Lexi wondered why Tom sounded put out. "You wanted Muddy Paws to help, didn't you? That's why you phoned us."

"Yeah, but . . ." Tom's voice trailed off then the phone went dead.

There wasn't much time to wonder about this because soon after the phone call ended, Fred strode back into the outhouse. "You did a good job," he told the girls when he saw the empty bottle. "But you see how long it takes?"

Lily nodded. "I got pins and needles in my legs from staying in one place too long."

"That's the problem," Fred pointed out. "Hand-rearing a lamb takes time and patience. As a rule, I've got plenty of patience. But right now I'm rushed off my feet with the lambing season and I don't have the time."

Lexi glanced at Lily who was settling Snowdrop back into her straw bed. Lily looked back at her and saw what she was thinking. "I – we . . ." she began.

". . . *We've* got time," Lexi said simply. "We could take Snowdrop back to Sea View."

"We definitely could!" Lily agreed.

Together they would make a bed for Snowdrop close to the kitchen stove. They would feed her four times a day. She would grow big and strong . . .

"Hmm." Fred hesitated. He gazed at

Snowdrop happily settled after her feed and thought of the two pregnant ewes about to give birth any minute now, of sleepless nights ahead waiting for others to be born. "It's true I can't be in more than one place at once," he murmured.

"Please let us take Snowdrop home with us," Lily said. "Dad will give us a lift. We'll make a lovely, cosy bed for her."

"But it's a tricky job, hand-rearing an orphan lamb," Fred warned. "You might not succeed."

Lily and Lexi's hearts raced. They wanted to do it – they *believed* they could do it.

Fred looked hard at the girls – at Lily with her bright red scarf wound around her neck and blonde hair tied back in a ponytail, at Lexi's brown eyes pleading with him. "All right," he agreed. "Let's give it a go."

Chapter Seven

"I got here just in time," Matt remarked as he drove Lily, Lexi and Snowdrop down the hill. He switched on his windscreen wipers to clear away the snow. "The forecast said it was going to snow again – and sure enough, here it comes."

"Thanks, Dad." Lily realized that he'd taken time out from his busy morning to drive over to Lighthouse Cottages to collect a pet carrier from Miss Goodwin then driven straight on up the hill to Moor Top Farm.

As the wipers swished and the snow fell,

Lexi took a peek at Snowdrop snuggled on a blanket inside Dino's carrier. The lamb was asleep, her front legs folded under her and her sweet little chin resting on the blanket. By the time Matt pulled into the car park at Sea View Café, there was already two centimetres of fresh snow covering the drive.

Lily saw her mum standing at the café door and quickly jumped out of the car. "Mum, come and look. Mr Starling let us bring Snowdrop home. We're going to bottle-feed her. She's really sweet. Come and look!"

"Quickly then," Jo agreed. "I've got no customers right now – thanks to this wonderful weather!"

So Jo and Lily followed Matt and Lexi through the snow into the cottage, where Alfie had been waiting patiently.

Matt set the pet carrier down on the floor

71

close to the stove. "Stay back, Alfie," he said firmly.

Afie retreated into a corner and settled down to watch.

Lily opened the carrier door and wrapped the blanket around Snowdrop before she lifted her out.

Snowdrop looked around with sleepy eyes then gave a small bleat.

"Cute," Jo smiled. "I *am* allowed to say that, aren't I?"

Lexi nodded then plucked up courage to ask a hard question. "The thing is, Aunty Jo – you don't like Muddy Paws to keep animals in the house, but . . ."

"But the kitchen is warm and we can't use the shed in the paddock like we normally do because it's freezing cold out there," Lily said quickly.

"So can we keep Snowdrop here in the kitchen?" Lexi asked.

The girls held their breaths and waited.

"Hmmm." Jo came up to Snowdrop and softly stroked her head.

Ba-a-a-a! Snowdrop opened her mouth and licked her lips with her pink tongue.

"She looks hungry," Jo said.

"She won't be any trouble, honestly!" Lexi pleaded. "We'll stay up with her during the night and feed her. You won't have to do anything."

"Please!" Lily added.

Jo's eyes softened as she tickled Snowdrop under the chin. "That sounds like a very good plan," she agreed.

* * *

"OK, Alfie, we're going to turf you out of your bed," Lexi explained.

"We're giving Snowdrop your basket if that's OK," Lily told him. "You can sleep here in the corner, on your own blanket. Help us keep an eye on Snowdrop."

"Uncle Matt is going to bring blow-up beds into the kitchen for me and Lily." Busily refolding Snowdrop's blanket to make it fit the dog basket while Lily cradled the lamb in her arms, Lexi explained the new routine. "Not yet though – it's only one o'clock in the afternoon, so there's ages to go before it gets dark."

When Lexi had finished making the bed for Snowdrop, Lily lowered her into the basket. "Oh, I just remembered something," she said with a little gasp.

"Kylie!" Lexi guessed.

"Yes, we told Mr Bolton that we'd dog-sit for him again this afternoon. He's going to the cinema to watch the latest James Bond movie."

"But we can't do it – not with Snowdrop here." Lexi frowned. Muddy Paws never let people down. Once they'd promised an owner they would do something, they always kept that promise.

Lily sighed. "No, we can't have Kylie charging around everywhere, growling at everyone and scaring Snowdrop. She's not like Alfie – she wouldn't understand."

Snoozing quietly in the corner, Alfie opened one eye and wagged his tail.

"She'd be yipping and yapping, chasing Alfie around the table, jumping up . . ." Lexi could just imagine the chaos.

The girls couldn't decide what to do.

"Problem?" Matt asked when he looked in on the girls. He'd been helping Jo tidy up in the café and knocked snow off his boots as he came inside, bringing a blast of cold air with him.

"Kylie," Lily muttered.

"Kylie and Snowdrop – they don't mix," Lexi explained.

Luckily at that moment the phone rang and Matt answered it. He listened then nodded. "OK, Arthur – I'll tell Lexi and Lily. Thanks for letting us know."

Glancing out of the window at the snowflakes whirling in the wind, Lily thought she knew what her dad was going to tell them. "Mr Bolton won't drive to Mellingham in the snow," she guessed. "He doesn't need us to dog-sit Kylie after all."

Matt nodded. "Crisis over. Now all you have to do is concentrate on feeding Snowdrop and helping her to grow big and strong."

"So we have to make a timetable," Lily decided straight after lunch. She took pen and paper, plus a ruler, and began work, ruling lines to form columns and writing the days of the week at the head of each column. Then she ruled horizontal lines and went down the left-hand side of the page, writing different times. "Twelve o'clock midnight, six o'clock in the morning, twelve o'clock midday and six o'clock in the evening."

"Every six hours." Lexi agreed it was a good idea to write down Snowdrop's feeding times. "Two pints for each feed. We can tick a box when we've finished. That way we'll keep track of how much milk she's had."

"And Mr Starling gave us this." Lily tapped a box with the tip of her pen. The label on the box said "'Lamb Starter

Grower'". It contained a powder which they had to mix in with Snowdrop's milk. "We mustn't forget that."

"We won't," Lexi promised. "We're going to do this right." Leaving Lily to work on the feeding chart at the table, she crouched beside Snowdrop's basket. "Everything's OK," she murmured. "Muddy Paws is looking after you. You're going to be fine."

* * *

By teatime on Saturday, snow was thick on the ground. Jo closed the café early and by the time Snowdrop's six o'clock feed was due, she and Matt were preparing home-made burgers and mash for the family meal.

"Get that, can you?" Matt asked Lily when the phone rang.

Lily and Lexi were measuring white powder from the packet and carefully tipping

it into Snowdrop's bottle of milk. "Sorry, Dad – we can't do it right now."

"It's OK – I'll do it." Jo broke off from cooking and picked up the phone. "Yes, Tom, they're here," she said. "But they're busy feeding the lamb . . . yes, OK, wait a moment."

"Tom Starling?" Lexi asked.

Jo nodded and handed over the phone. "He says it's important."

So Lexi took the phone and waited to hear what Tom had to say.

"Hi, Lexi. How's Snowdrop?" he asked.

"Good," she replied. "We're just about to feed her."

"Has she settled in OK?"

"Yes, fine."

"Did you remember to add the Starter Grower to the milk?"

"Yes, Tom, we did."

"Only, it's important she has the concentrated feed now that she's nearly a week old."

"We know, Tom. Your dad explained everything to us. You can relax."

But that's what poor Tom couldn't do.

His croaky voice kept on asking questions – was Snowdrop warm enough, who was going to take care of her during the night, did they realize that the bottle had to be sterilized every time they used it?

Yes, yes and yes, Lexi replied. "Honestly, Tom, Snowdrop is curled up asleep in Alfie's bed. We'll pick her up to feed her then pop her straight back in the basket afterwards."

"Good." Tom still sounded worried. "You know it's snowed again up here on the moor?"

"Here too," she told him.

"The wind has blown it into deep drifts. It means we're cut off until they can get a snowplough up here."

"Cut off?" Lexi echoed. "So it's a good job we brought Snowdrop home when we did."

"But it means Dad and I can't get down to Sea View Cottage if . . . if anything goes wrong."

"But it won't," Lexi assured him as she watched Lily take Snowdrop out of the basket and tuck her under her arm, ready to feed. Nevertheless, she felt a small knot form in her tummy. "We're taking good care of Snowdrop," she insisted. "She's going to be fine."

"OK, good – thanks," Tom said quickly before he hung up.

Absolutely fine! Lexi told herself. But, despite what she'd said to Tom Starling, she had to admit it was scary, taking sole charge of a lamb that was only five and a half days old!

Chapter Eight

It was strange to be sleeping on blow-up beds in the kitchen.

"These beds feel kind of bouncy," Lily whispered to Lexi once the lights were out. Snowdrop was sleeping peacefully in Alfie's basket and Alfie was snoozing under the table.

Lexi giggled as she snuggled into her sleeping bag. She checked that she had a torch nearby, ready for the midnight feed. "It's like camping."

"Only without the tent," Lily agreed.

They fell silent for a while, then Lexi said, "Lily, are you asleep?"

"No," came the reply.

"Me neither," Lexi sighed. "Why can't we get to sleep?"

"We're too excited. Well, not excited exactly – more *nervous*."

"Yeah, we don't want to fall asleep and miss Snowdrop's next feed."

Lily lay on her back and stared up into the darkness. If she listened hard she could hear Alfie and Snowdrop's soft, drawn-out breathing. Otherwise there was silence. "All we have to do is get up at midnight and mix the feed."

"Then dunk the bottle into a pan of hot water to heat it up."

"Then give it to Snowdrop," Lily murmured. It was simple – no problem.

"Lexi, are you still awake?"

She waited but she found there was no answer, only the sound of gentle snoring from Lexi's blow-up bed.

* * *

"Whuh – what happened?" Lexi woke in the pitch dark to the feel of Alfie's rough tongue licking her cheek. She reached for her torch and switched it on.

"Uh-huh?" A sleepy Lily grunted from her sleeping bag. "What time is it?"

Lexi shone the torch at her watch. "Almost twelve o'clock – time for Snowdrop's feed. Alfie woke me up. Good boy, Alfie!"

Wagging his tail, Alfie's paws pitter-pattered over the stone-flagged floor to the spot by the stove where Snowdrop lay. The little lamb raised her head and began her flat, high-pitched bleat. *Ba-a-a-ah!*

"It's OK, Alfie won't hurt you," Lexi said. "He's your friend." Quickly she turned on the light while Lily, still in her sleeping bag, rolled out of bed.

"Ouch!" Lily said as she hit the floor. Then she unzipped her bag and joined Lexi by the sink. "It's a good job Alfie woke us. It's as if he knew it was time for Snowdrop's feed."

"Alfie's a genius," Lexi grinned and together the girls poured milk and powder into the bottle. Lexi screwed the teat into place then Lily shook the mixture. Soon they were ready to feed Snowdrop.

"Your turn," Lily told Lexi. She watched as Lexi lifted Snowdrop from her bed and pressed the teat against her lips. She smiled as Snowdrop grabbed the teat between her lips then sucked greedily.

Lexi smiled back. Little Snowdrop's body was warm and soft. She was feeding well. Everything was good.

* * *

"Just look at this!" Matt said to Jo as he opened the kitchen door next morning. It wasn't quite daylight when they'd crept downstairs to see how the girls were getting on with their lamb-sitting task.

Jo peered into the kitchen. Lexi and Lily were snuggled so deep in their sleeping bags that only the tops of their heads showed. Over by the stove, Snowdrop lay fast asleep.

"Look at Alfie," Matt murmured.

It took Jo a while to make him out in the dim, dawn light. At last she spotted him curled up close to Snowdrop's basket, snoozing and sharing the warmth from the stove.

"Aah!" Jo sighed.

"Alfie and Snowdrop are the best of friends!" Matt smiled.

And Jo and Matt closed the door on the peaceful scene and went quietly back upstairs to bed.

* * *

"Yeah, Tom – everything's cool." Lexi took the first phone call of the morning. "Snowdrop is glugging down all her feeds, no problem."

It was Sunday, so after the phone call Lexi and Lily trudged with Alfie through the snow to the school caretaker's house.

"Please can you let us into our classroom?" Lily asked Mr Harrison, whose sandy-haired dog, Scruffy, came to the door with him. Scruffy and Alfie sniffed and wagged their tails while the humans talked. "We have to clean out Smudge's cage."

"We couldn't do it yesterday – we had to fetch an orphan lamb from Moor Top Farm." Lexi felt proud as she told the caretaker what Muddy Paws had done.

Mr Harrison put on his coat without grumbling and walked across the playground to open up the school.

Lily and Lexi made snowballs and threw them for Alfie and Scruffy. They laughed

when the dogs tried to catch them and they broke apart. The dogs looked puzzled – what happened, where did the ball go?

Then the girls took off their boots in the entrance and went quickly to the classroom. The squeak-squeak of Smudge's exercise wheel told them that all was well with the school hamster. They chatted with Mr Harrison as they took Smudge out of his cage. Lexi held him while Lily took out his old bed of straw and scrunched-up newspaper.

"Who'd have thought we'd get this much snow at this time of year?" the caretaker said. "The farmer's won't like it – not during lambing season. I hope they don't lose too many lambs to the cold and frost."

"We just got Snowdrop out in time," Lily explained.

"Snowdrop?" Mr Harrison asked.

"The orphan lamb we told you about." Seeing that Lily had finished making a fresh bed for Smudge, Lexi put the hamster back in his cage and fastened the door. "Thanks, Mr Harrison. Sorry we have to dash."

"That's OK," he smiled. "You Muddy Paws girls are always busy, so run on ahead. I'll lock up after you."

* * *

"Hi, Tom. Yeah, everything's fine."

It was Lily's turn to answer the phone. On the way home from the school, she and Lexi had called in at the village shop to buy cat food for Miss Goodwin, who had left a message to say she was stranded at Lighthouse Cottages.

The old lady had thanked them for struggling through the snow drifts then given them biscuits and hot chocolate. "I hope Dino's pet carrier came in useful," she said.

"Very," Lexi had told her. "We'll bring it back to you after we've taken Snowdrop home to Moor Top Farm."

"When Tom is better," Lily had added, and for a few moments she'd felt sad about the idea of having to let Snowdrop go.

Now it was after Snowdrop's midday feed and once more she was on the phone to Tom Starling.

"You're sure you're giving her all her feeds?" he asked. "You're not missing any out?"

"Would we?" Lily replied. Honestly, did Tom actually think they would forget to feed Snowdrop?

"OK – just checking," he muttered before he abruptly ended the call.

That afternoon, Snowdrop ventured out of her basket for the very first time. She'd been awake since lunch-time, warily watching Alfie as he came in and out of kitchen, all the time wagging his tail.

At last, when Alfie had settled under the table for a nap, Snowdrop raised herself from her blanket then put a timid foot on to the stone floor.

Sitting at the table, keeping the lamb's feeding chart up to date, Lily nudged Lexi.

"Oh, you're so brave!" Lexi murmured. She grinned as Snowdrop stepped out of her bed.

Snowdrop shook herself then arched her back. All of a sudden she sprang high into the air – once, twice, three times.

"Whoo!" Lily said. "She's gambolling!"

95

"Gambling?" Lexi asked with a puzzled frown.

"Not 'gambling' – 'gam*boll*ing' – it's what lambs do! They skip and run and gambol across the field."

"Anyway, it's cute," Lexi sighed. "And it means she's happy – right?"

* * *

"Yeah, Tom, we'll stay with her all night tonight – like we did last night." It was dark when Lily took Tom's last call of the day. "You still sound croaky, by the way. How's your throat?"

"Getting better," he said then fired more questions about Snowdrop down the phone. Had they increased the feed to two pints? How was she doing on the Starter Grower? Was she putting on weight?

"Everything's fine," Lily assured him.

"We'll feed her at midnight then at six tomorrow."

"So what will you do when you have to go to school tomorrow?"

Lily had already thought ahead. "We'll nip home at lunch-time and feed her," she said. "Don't worry, Tom. Go to bed and sleep. Get better as quick as you can."

Chapter Nine

"You two look bright and chirpy this morning," Mrs Taylor told Lexi and Lily when they arrived at school.

They nodded and while the teacher took the register, they gave Emma, Charlie and Sam an update on Snowdrop.

"Cool!" Emma said when Lily described how Alfie had made friends with the orphan lamb.

"You should have brought her to school," Charlie told Lexi when she explained how brave and tame Snowdrop was getting.

Lexi shook her head. "This is real life, Charlie. It's not like the nursery rhyme – lambs can't follow you everywhere, especially not to school."

"I bet Tom's jealous of you hand-rearing his lamb," was Sam's opinion.

Lily thought for a while then gave a small nod. Of course – that explained all the questions and the sudden way Tom broke off his phone calls. "You're probably right."

All through the morning they found it hard to concentrate on work and the second the lunch bell rang they grabbed their jackets and headed for home.

* * *

"Hi, girls!" Jo called from the door of her café. "I have hot soup waiting for you whenever you're ready. It's another cold day so you'll need something to warm you up."

"Thanks, Aunty Jo!" Lexi sped down the path towards the cottage with Lily hard on her heels.

"Hi, Lexi, hi, Lily!" Matt opened the window to his upstairs office and yelled a greeting.

"How's Snowdrop?" Lily called back. "Has she been OK?"

"Right as rain, as far as I know."

"That means 'yes'," Lily told Lexi. "No, don't ask – it doesn't make sense to me either. That's just Dad being peculiar."

Lexi grinned. Once inside the warm kitchen, she greeted Alfie then unzipped her jacket and set about mixing Snowdrop's lunchtime feed. "Have you been looking after Snowdrop for us?" she asked her excited pet.

There was plenty of tail wagging from

100

Alfie and a little bleat from Snowdrop.

"Hey, Snowdrop, are you going to get up and have a stretch before your feed?" Lily wanted to know.

Ba-a-a-a!

Snowdrop didn't try to get up from her bed so Lily lifted her out instead. "It's OK – it's only us," she told her as she felt the lamb tremble. "Don't be scared."

But Snowdrop's little body was still

shaking when Lexi gave Lily the warm bottle, and when Lily pressed the teat against her lips, at first she didn't want to open her mouth.

"Hmm." Lexi watched with her head to one side. "Maybe she's not hungry."

"But she should be," Lily argued. "It's six hours since her last feed." She waited patiently until she saw Snowdrop stick out her tongue to lick the dribbles escaping from the teat. "That's better," she murmured. "Good – now you just suck like you usually do."

It took longer than usual but eventually Lexi looked at the bottle and saw that Snowdrop had taken two thirds of her feed.

"She doesn't want any more," Lily decided, gently lowering Snowdrop back into her basket.

"She's a little sleepy-head," Lexi said as she watched Snowdrop's head droop and her eyelids close. "Come on, Lily – we have to get a move on."

So they told Alfie to keep an eye on things while they were gone and shouted goodbye to Matt on their way out of the cottage.

"What about the soup?" Jo called from the café doorway as they dashed down the path.

"Sorry, Mum – no time!" Lily answered.

They ran fast and got back to school in the nick of time – just as the bell rang for the start of afternoon lessons.

* * *

A visitor came into school to tell Year 6 about her career as a fire-fighter. Normally Lily and Lexi would have been fascinated but today they weren't. PE didn't interest them either – their minds were too fixed on Snowdrop to care who won their game of five-a-side soccer. Back in the classroom, even Smudge peeking through the bars of his cage and twitching his nose and whiskers didn't amuse.

It was only when lessons ended and they were on their way back to Sea View that Lexi and Lily could really concentrate on what had been bothering them all afternoon.

"Snowdrop's going to be OK," Lexi insisted as they passed the post office overlooking the village square. "What's it matter if she doesn't drink the whole bottle once in a while?"

"That's right," Lily agreed. But she couldn't help remembering how, even though it was warm in the kitchen, Snowdrop had trembled when she held her in her arms.

She was glad when Sea View Café came into view and they could check in on the little orphan. "She's going to be fine."

* * *

Jo was still busy in the café when they arrived home and Matt had left a note to say he'd had to drop off a delivery of tea to a shop in Mellingham. "Back around six," he wrote.

So the house was empty except for Alfie and Snowdrop.

"Hi, Alfie – what's wrong?" Lexi asked as soon as she saw him. He didn't come up and wag his tail. Instead, he lay quietly beside Snowdrop's basket.

Lily crouched beside the lamb and her heart skipped a beat. "What's wrong?" she whispered.

Snowdrop lay there, eyes half closed, head resting on the blanket.

"She's breathing very fast." Lily noticed. She felt scared as she reached out to stroke the top of the lamb's head. "And she feels hot."

"Does that mean she's sick?" Lexi wondered. "What does it mean if a lamb is hot and not breathing very well? Wait – I'm going to look it up."

She went quickly to the computer on the kitchen table and entered "Sick lambs" into the search engine. Lily stayed beside Snowdrop's basket.

"Does her tummy feel bloated?" Lexi asked, reading from a list of symptoms she'd brought up onscreen.

"No," Lily replied.

"Does it look like she's got diarrhoea?"

Lily checked Snowdrop's bedding and shook her head. "What do you think it is?"

she asked, her heart pounding against her chest.

"'Rapid breathing and a high temperature.'" Quickly Lexi read down the list. It seemed to take forever and then Lily heard her gasp, "Oh no!"

"What? Tell me." By this time Lily herself was shaking.

Lexi swallowed hard then turned off the computer. Her face was pale as she joined Lily. Together they gazed down at sick little Snowdrop.

"I think she's got pneumonia," Lexi said quietly. "Lily, this is serious!"

Chapter Ten

Pneumonia! Lily and Lexi's heads were in a whirl. When people got pneumonia they sometimes died, and they were scared it might be the same with animals.

"We have to save Snowdrop!" Lexi declared.

"We have to take her to a vet," Lily agreed.

But how? Lily's dad wasn't here to give them a lift and her mum couldn't leave the café.

"We're stuck," Lexi groaned.

"What if we call Moor Top Farm?" Lily

wondered. "Maybe Fred can help."

Lexi shook her head. "They're snowed in, remember. But at least we should call them and tell them what's happening."

Lily was the one to pick up the phone. When Tom answered, she spoke with a shaky voice. "Hi, Tom. We've got a problem."

"It's Snowdrop, isn't it?" he said quickly.

"We think she's sick," Lily confessed. "It could be pneumonia."

There was a shocked silence then Tom spoke angrily. "I told Dad he shouldn't have sent her away. I knew something like this would happen."

Lily did her best to calm him down. "We're not sure yet. We need to take her to a vet. Do you know which one?"

Tom ignored the question. "I said I could

look after her, but Dad didn't listen."

"You couldn't – you were poorly," Lily reminded him.

"I could have. I *wanted* to."

"Listen, Tom – who's your vet?"

"His name's Marcus."

"Marcus who?"

"Marcus Williams."

Lily repeated the name to Lexi who wrote it down. "Have you got his number?" she asked Tom.

"613452. If it's pneumonia you have to keep Snowdrop warm and get her to drink lots of water."

"We will, I promise." As Lily spoke to Tom, she heard a knock at the door. She was still talking as Lexi rushed to answer it.

"And give her a baby aspirin," Tom went on. "That's what we do when lambs get pneumonia. Then we take them to see the vet."

"OK, we'll do it," Lily promised. "Don't worry, Tom – we'll try . . ." The phone clicked and went dead. ". . . our hardest to save Snowdrop," she said.

* * *

Charlie Golding came into the kitchen with a gift of a dozen fresh eggs laid by the hens on his smallholding. He put them down on the table. "Hi, girls – how are you doing? Are you still busy with Muddy Paws?" He took one look at their strained faces and his cheerful smile melted. "Whatever's the matter?" he asked.

Lily was too busy giving Snowdrop an aspirin to answer and Lexi was too worried to say anything so she pointed to Snowdrop instead.

Straight away Charlie understood. "That's not right," he muttered, running a hand through his thick hair. "Let me take a look – yes, she seems listless, poor little thing."

"You know about lambs," Lily said eagerly. "You have them at Lane's End. What do you do when they're sick?"

"Take them to Marcus Williams," Charlie

answered quickly. "He's very experienced with farm animals."

"Good – that's what Tom said. We want to do that but Mum's busy and Dad's not here," Lily explained.

"I'll take you," Charlie said, quick as a flash.

So Lily wrapped Snowdrop in her blanket while Lexi ran to fetch the pet carrier. Five minutes later they were in Charlie's old Volvo and heading along the lane towards Mellingham.

"I can't go too fast," Charlie explained as he put on the brakes and skidded to a halt at a T-junction. "The roads are icy and it's starting to snow again."

He was slowly turning right when a figure on a bike sped down the hill towards them.

"Look out – he's going to crash into us!"

Lily made Charlie brake again.

The cyclist hurtled towards them.

"It's Tom!" Lexi exclaimed. She wound down the window and yelled at him as he took the corner at breakneck speed. "Tom – it's us! We've got Snowdrop in the car with us!"

Tom stopped so suddenly that his bike skidded sideways and fell into the ditch. He jumped clear just in time. "I came to help," he muttered as he brushed snow from his jacket.

"Charlie's taking us to the vet's." Opening the door, Lily told him to jump in the car. "You're sick," she reminded him. "You shouldn't even be out."

"How did you get through the snow?" Lexi demanded.

Tom was breathless. "I walked along the

wall tops to keep above the drifts," he told them. "When I got to our neighbour's farm lower down the hill, I borrowed a bike. The roads were clear after that."

"That's amazing!" Lexi was impressed. And it made her realize how much Tom must care about Snowdrop. She peered in at her, lying on her side in the pet carrier. "Come on, Charlie – we need to get a move on!"

* * *

It took twenty minutes to drive to the outskirts of Mellingham. During all that time Snowdrop lay without moving inside the carrier.

"Her breathing's all wrong," Lily whispered as she watched the little lamb's ribs rise and fall rapidly.

"Her eyes are closed," Lexi said.

Tom said nothing at all.

"Here we are," Charlie said at last. He pulled off the main road into a car park next to a big old house with a notice saying "Williams Veterinary Practice" over the doorway.

Quickly the girls unloaded Snowdrop from the car and rushed her into the clinic. Tom ran ahead and opened the door.

"It's one of our lambs – she's sick," he told the nurse standing behind a desk in a small reception area.

"She can't breathe properly," Lily added. Her heart thudded as she and Lexi set the pet carrier on the ground.

"It's an emergency," Lexi insisted.

The nurse took one quick look at Snowdrop then hurried to fetch the vet. Marcus Williams came out of his treatment room – an old man with white hair and round-rimmed glasses. "Bring the lamb in here," he told them. "Lift her out of the carrier and lay her on the table – gently does it."

Lily and Lexi stood back to let Tom lift Snowdrop on to the treatment table. Snowdrop tried to raise her head but she was too weak. She looked little and helpless under the bright light.

"First we'll take her temperature," the vet decided. He worked quickly and calmly. "Yes, that's very high. Now let me have a feel of her tummy."

Lexi, Lily and Tom held their breaths as Marcus Williams carried out his examination.

'She's not bloated so we can say there's nothing wrong with her stomach or her digestion. And it's not a gut problem either. But she's definitely dehydrated. That means the fever is causing rapid fluid loss."

Lily and Lexi tried hard to follow what the vet was saying. When they glanced at Tom, they saw that he'd gritted his teeth and pursed up his lips in an effort to hold back the tears. It made them both want to cry too.

"The shallow, rapid breathing tells me what this is," Marcus went on. He covered Snowdrop with her blanket and looked up at Tom, Lexi and Lily. He confirmed what they'd been afraid of all along. "This little lamb has a lung infection – yes, I'd say we have a severe case of pneumonia."

Chapter Eleven

The nurse led Lexi, Lily and Tom back into the waiting area while Marcus Williams worked to save Snowdrop's life.

"He'll give her an antibiotic to fight the infection," Charlie explained. "He may even put her on a fluid drip and keep her in overnight." He went on to say that he'd phoned Lily's mum and Tom's dad and told them where they all were.

Lexi and Lily nodded then sat on a narrow bench while Tom went to the window and stared out at the softly falling snow.

"Try not to worry too much," Charlie told them. "It's common for lambs to get pneumonia when the weather's this cold and Marcus knows exactly what's needed to make her better."

Lily nodded again and tried to put on a brave smile. But inside she was scared. "Snowdrop's so skinny and little," she said in a shaky voice.

There was a long silence then Lexi spoke. "Muddy Paws should have looked after her better," she said with a long sigh. "This is our fault, Lily. And now she might even die!"

* * *

It was dark when Charlie drove them home.

"Snowdrop is doing OK," the nurse had told them. "But Marcus would like to keep her here overnight so we can keep an eye on her."

So they'd left without seeing the patient, with only the scary memory of her lying motionless on the treatment table under a bright light.

They drove in miserable silence until they reached the turn-off for Moor Top Farm where they found Fred Starling in his Land-Rover, waiting to drive Tom home.

When Fred saw Charlie's car, he walked across. "At least it stopped snowing long enough to get a snowplough up our lane," he told Charlie. "And they reckon it's going to thaw tomorrow."

As Tom got out and joined his dad, Lily and Lexi sat glumly in the back seat. How could the men talk about the weather while Snowdrop lay seriously ill?

"You'll be glad to open the petting farm
again," Charlie said to Fred before they said
goodbye.

Lexi and Lily watched Tom follow his dad
to the Land-Rover and climb into the
passenger seat. Then, to their surprise, he
jumped out and ran back to Charlie's car.
He knocked on the window and Lexi
opened it.

"What?" she asked.

"Nothing," he began, his face flushed and his voice quiet. "I was thinking – I just wanted to say . . ."

"Come on, Tom, spit it out," Charlie urged.

Tom cleared his throat. "Lexi, what you said – about it being your fault."

"We're sorry – we really are!" Lily interrupted.

"It wasn't," Tom argued. "Snowdrop was probably sick before she left Moor Top Farm."

Lexi blinked and Lily swallowed hard.

"I've been thinking about it. You know our outhouse? It's freezing in there."

This was true. They waited for Tom to go on.

"That must have been where she caught pneumonia," Tom told them. "It's got nothing to do with Muddy Paws. In fact . . ." He faltered then made himself go on. "In fact, if the medicine works and Snowdrop does get better, it'll be because of you."

"How do you work that out?" Lexi asked, hardly able to believe what she was hearing.

"You're the ones who saw she was ill and took her to the vet," Tom explained. "If she lives, you'll have saved her life!"

* * *

That night Lily and Lexi put away the blow-up beds then settled Alfie back into his basket by the stove.

"I know," Lexi sighed as she stroked Alfie's soft fur. "You're sad about Snowdrop, just like us."

Alfie gave a half-hearted wag of his tail and looked up at the girls as they got ready to go upstairs to bed.

"Try to get some sleep," Jo told Lexi and Lily kindly. "You did everything you could for Snowdrop."

"And let's hope she pulls through," Matt added as he kissed the girls goodnight.

But up in their bedrooms, snuggled under warm duvets, they both lay awake thinking of Snowdrop.

If only we'd taken her to the vet's before it got so bad, Lily thought. But how could they have known before today that anything was wrong?

And what went through Lexi's mind was that poor little Snowdrop didn't deserve this. She should be out in the fields at Moor Top Farm, playing with the other lambs.

It was the longest night of their lives and when they got dressed and went downstairs next morning they told Matt that they didn't want any breakfast.

"Have some toast and marmalade," he insisted. And he didn't let them leave for school before they'd had two slices each.

"Dad, if you hear anything about Snowdrop this morning, will you come to school and tell us?" Lily begged at the door of the cottage.

"It doesn't matter if it's bad news – we just want to know," Lexi insisted.

He promised he would but still they dragged their feet along the lane into the village and into the school playground. Emma asked them to play football until the bell went for the start of lessons, but both Lily and Lexi shook their heads. Instead they sat on a bench with Sam, quietly telling him the sad news about Snowdrop.

"Tom was as worried as us," Lily told

him. "He knows pneumonia is serious."

It was Sam who pointed to the gate and said, 'Talking of Tom – he must be feeling better 'cos here he comes now!"

Lexi gasped then grabbed Lily's arm and squeezed it tight. They watched as Tom walked towards them. Had his dad spoken to Marcus Williams this morning? Did Tom look happy or sad?

Tom was looking down at the ground. They couldn't tell what he was thinking.

"Tom?" Lexi said, her heart racing.

He looked up – right at them – and gave them the news. "Snowdrop is out of danger!" he announced, letting a big, broad grin spread across his face.

Chapter Twelve

That day the thaw set in. Green clumps of daffodil shoots broke through the melting snow and birds began to sing again in the trees.

"Snowdrop's doing well," Tom told Lexi and Lily. "She's getting stronger."

On Wednesday he came to school and proudly told the class that four more lambs had been born at Moor Top Farm.

"How's Snowdrop?" Lexi asked him.

"Better. She can come home soon."

"When?" Lily asked.

"This afternoon. Dad's going to collect her."

Lily looked at Lexi and Lexi looked at Lily. "When can we come and see her?" they said.

"How about after school today?" Tom answered with a grin.

* * *

"How will you get up to Moor Top?" Jo asked the girls when they rushed into Sea View Café and dumped their schoolbags on the floor. "Your dad's out so he can't take you."

"Bikes!" Lexi said.

"We'll take Alfie." Lily was already heading across the yard. "Gotta go, Mum – bye!"

So Alfie trotted ahead of the bikes as Lily and Lexi pedalled up the steep hill. When he reached the gate to Moor Top Farm he sat on the grass and waited.

"Phew!" Lexi was out of breath and her legs ached from pedalling.

Lily was close behind. She leaned her bike against the gatepost and together they hurried across the car park towards the barn.

Back at the gate, Alfie sat patiently. He gave a little yap.

"Oops!" Lexi had forgotten about him. "Come!" she called. And Alfie scampered to join them.

Fred Starling came out of the barn to greet them. "I saw you arrive," he said. "Tom's expecting you."

"Where is he?" Lily asked, almost tripping over herself in her hurry to see Snowdrop.

"There he is!" Lexi spotted him inside the barn. Tom was tipping cabbage leaves into

Darwin's enclosure and the giant tortoise lumbered across the pen towards them.

"But where's Snowdrop?" Lily wanted to know.

"She's not far away," Fred promised as he went on across the yard towards the house.

"Where?" Lexi looked everywhere. She saw fluffy chickens in their heated glass box and Honeysuckle, the Gloucester Old Spot, in her pen. "Tom!" she called, "we've come to see . . ."

Alfie wagged his tail then put his nose to the ground and followed a trail around the side of Honeysuckle's pen. Lexi and Lily went after him.

". . . Snowdrop!" Lily cried out in delight.

The little lamb sat on a pile of loose straw, her legs tucked under her, head to one side. *Ba-a-a-a!* she said.

Then she got up onto her skinny legs and skipped with Alfie across the floor. She ran and jumped, chased Alfie around in circles, grew tired and came to join Lexi and Lily. *Ba-a-a!*

"It's true – she's better!" Lexi sighed.

"Completely better," Lily agreed.

Lexi and Lily sank to their knees to stroke Snowdrop. They cuddled, petted and squeezed until Tom came over to rescue her. Laughing, he picked her up, tucked her under his arm and told the others to follow him.

"Where are we going?" Lily asked. Her heart felt so happy she thought it would burst.

"I'm going to put her in the field with the other lambs," he told her.

So Tom and Snowdrop, Alfie, Lily and

Lexi walked together out into the sloping field where a dozen lambs skipped and played.

Tom put Snowdrop down. She shook herself then looked up at the bright blue sky. She put her head down and sniffed at the green grass.

"Go on," Tom urged gently. "Go and play."

Snowdrop lifted a leg and took her first step into the big wide world. Then another.

"I think she likes it," Lexi murmured as Snowdrop grew braver. She watched the lamb take a little run and then a jump. "Look – she's gam*boll*ing."

Lily smiled. Snowdrop was definitely well again. She was out in the open air, learning to play.

"What do you think?" Tom asked Lily and Lexi as Alfie sat quietly by Lexi's side.

But they didn't have time to answer before Alfie stood up and gave a small bark. He'd spotted trouble.

Lexi saw what was wrong. There was a dog without an owner at the gate – a small black and brown dog whom she recognized. "Uh-oh!" she warned.

"Oh no, it's Kylie," Lily groaned. The King Charles spaniel had squeezed under the gate into the field and there was no sign of Arthur Bolton to call her back.

Kylie yipped and yapped, ears flopping as she charged towards the nearest sheep.

But Alfie leaped into action. He darted across the field to cut Kylie off and chase her back towards the gate just as Arthur appeared over the brow of the hill.

Grrr! Kylie crouched low and bared her teeth.

Grrr! Alfie growled back. He cornered Kylie until her flustered owner arrived.

"I'm so sorry!" Arthur called. "She ran away when I called her."

"Sorry, Tom – he needs help," Lily told Tom.

"Kylie has problems," Lexi agreed.

Tom nodded. "See you tomorrow."

"Yeah, Tom, see you!"

Lily and Lexi had work to do.

"Kylie, sit!" Lexi told the little spaniel in her strictest voice.

"Kylie, stay!" Lily insisted.

Grrrrr! the problem pooch snapped back.

Lexi grinned at Lily and Lily grinned back. It was Muddy Paws to the rescue one more time!

FREE MUDDY PAWS SCRAPBOOK

Find out what happens to Lexi and Lily in *Rocking with Roxy and Rosie* – another Muddy Paws adventure – and receive a FREE Muddy Paws scrapbook! The scrapbook is the ideal place for you to put pictures of all your favourite animals and pets. Plus there are activities perfect for all Muddy Paws fans!

To receive your Muddy Paws scrapbook, you need to collect two tokens. One is below and you'll find other tokens in the rest of the Muddy Paws series. Then simply fill in the form on this page and send it to us with both tokens and we'll send you your FREE Muddy Paws scrapbook!

Send one completed form and two tokens to: The Muddy Paws Scrapbook Offer, The Marketing Department, Hachette Children's Books, 338 Euston Road, London, NW1 3BH

Closing date: 30 April 2014

TERMS AND CONDITIONS

(1) Open to UK and Republic of Ireland residents only (2) You must provide the email address of a parent or guardian for your entry to be valid (3) Photocopied tokens are not accepted (4) The form must be completed fully for your entry to be valid (5) Scrapbooks are distributed on a first come, first served basis while stocks last (6) No part of the offer is exchangeable for cash or any other offer (7) Please allow 28 days for delivery (8) Your details will only be used for the purposes of fulfilling this offer and, if you choose [see tick box below], to receive email newsletters about other great Hachette Children's books, and will never be shared with any third party.

- ✂ -

Please complete using capital letters (UK Residents Only)

FIRST NAME:

SURNAME:

DATE OF BIRTH: DD | MM | YYYY

ADDRESS LINE 1:

ADDRESS LINE 2:

ADDRESS LINE 3:

POSTCODE:

PARENT OR GUARDIAN'S EMAIL:

☐ I'm happy to receive email newsletters and information about other great Hachette Children's books (I can unsubscribe at any time).

ONE TOKEN

www.hachettechildrens.co